Eddie Pittman

Red's Planet

AMULET BOOKS
NEW YORK

Library of Congress Control Number: 2015946889

ISBN 978-1-4197-1907-3 (hardback) — ISBN 978-1-4197-1908-0 (paperback)

Printed and bound in China

10 9 8 7 6 5 4 3

ABRAMS The Art of Books
195 Broadway, New York, NY 10007
abramsbooks.com

To Mom and Dad—the storyteller and the artist, and my first inspirations

Thanks to:

Norm Fuetti, Joshua Pruett, Tom Richmond, Dan Povenmire, Swampy Marsh, Jeff Smith, Kim Roberson, Mike Maihack, Travis Hanson, Tom Dell'Aringa, Steve Ogden, and Broose Johnson for their support, encouragement, and help along the journey.

Travis Hanson, Jose Flores, Sean Balsano, Janelle Bell-Martin, and Ginny Pittman for color and production assistance.

The readers, commenters, and fans of the *Red's Planet* webcomic for keeping me going.

Chad W. Beckerman, Pam Notarantonio, and the whole team at Abrams.

Judy Hansen, my super-ninja agent.

Charlie Kochman, my amazing editor, for taking a chance on this little book.

And to my beautiful wife, Beth, and my amazing kids, Ginny and Teagan—my first and most important audience.

Chapter One
Thing from Another Planet

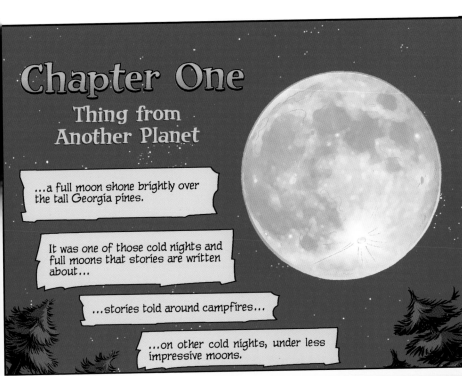

...a full moon shone brightly over the tall Georgia pines.

It was one of those cold nights and full moons that stories are written about...

...stories told around campfires...

...on other cold nights, under less impressive moons.

On a lonely country road, an even lonelier old pickup truck rambled along.

Down the lonely road of destiny.

Zeke Hainey was returning home from a weekend hunting trip.

His only companions: a cup of bad coffee

...his old hunting dog

...and a fading radio station.

"AW, C'MON! STOP THE **BORING** STUFF AND START READING THE **GOOD** PARTS, WILL YA!"

"WAIT JUST A MINUTE! YOU MEAN THE *ALIENS* TOOK THE *DOG?!*"

WHAT WOULD **ALIENS** WANT WITH AN **OLD** DOG, FOR CRYING OUT LOUD?!

WELL, IT **SAYS** HERE THEY TOOK THE OLD MAN, TOO!

SURE THEY DID! AND THAT'S **ANOTHER** THING...

THE MAN JUST GOT BACK FROM A **HUNTING TRIP**, RIGHT? AND **ALL** HE TAKES INTO THE WOODS TO CHECK OUT A **STRANGE** LIGHT IS...

A **TIRE IRON**?

ANYONE **ELSE** SEE A **PROBLEM** HERE?

NOT TO MENTION, IF **THEY** WERE **ALL** ALONE...

THEN **WHO** WAS AROUND TO TELL THE **STORY**?

WELL?

WHAT **IS** THAT MAGAZINE ANYWAY?

HEY!

GIMME!

UFO FANCY?!

UFOFancy

October 1979

Vol. 4 No. 8

ACTION RESEARCH REPORT Jimmy Carter's Alien Rabbit Encounter

THE DEVIL'S ...LE ...y Alien ...Y?

...LUSIVE ...HOTOS ...SUGGEST UFOS ...ARE GRAINY

...NANU-NANU: ...UFOS PROBE

TALK ABOUT YOUR **ANCIENT** ALIENS! HOW **OLD** IS THIS **THING**?!

IT'S LIKE FROM WAY BACK IN THE **1900S!**

11

EGGS. POACHED. LIGHTLY.

WITH *THREE* PIECES OF BACON, RAISIN TOAST, A *BELGIAN WAFFLE* COVERED IN STRAWBERRIES, A CHOCOLATE DONUT WITH *SPRINKLES*, FRENCH FRIES...

...AND A STACK OF CHOCOLATE CHIP PANCAKES *SLATHERED* IN *PEANUT BUTTER*.

I KNOW, *"GO SIT DOWN."*

18

UH...HEY...

...WILL YA **LOOK** AT WHAT I **DID**...

I WENT AND PUT ON THE **WRONG SHOES!**

AND I CANNOT WEAR **THESE** SHOES BECAUSE THEY ARE **NOT** SCHOOL **REGULATION** AS STATED IN THE COUNTY SCHOOL **DRESS CODE** SECTION 13, PARAGRAPH 4, AND I **QUOTE**...

...ALL STUDENTS **MUST** WEAR **APPROVED** WHITE, RUBBER-SOLED SHOES WITH FULL TOES AND HEELS AND THE AFOREMENTIONED SHOES **MUST** REMAIN TIED AT ALL TIMES UNDER THE PENALTY OF **DETENTION!**

ILLEGAL FOOTWEAR INCLUDES, BUT IS NOT LIMITED TO:

FLIP-FLOPS, SLINGBACKS, WINKLEPICKERS, SANDALS, SLIPPERS, SKATE SHOES, BEACH SHOES, MULES, PUMPS, CLOGS, MOCCASINS, CLEATS, SNOWSHOES, HORSESHOES, TAP SHOES, HEAVY, HIKING, CONSTRUCTION, COWBOY, COMBAT, *OR* GO-GO BOOTS *AND* **HIGH-TOP SNEAKERS!**

WHAT WILL I **DO** NOW?

WAIT A **MINUTE!** ARE **YOU** THINKING WHAT **I'M** THINKING?!

I'LL JUST **RUN** BACK HOME, CHANGE THESE SILLY SHOES, THEN CATCH UP WITH YOU KIDS **LATER!**

WHAT DO **YOU** KNOW ABOUT THE **TOOTH FAIRY**

STO... PUSHING.

MAN, I'D LOVE TO HAVE A **BACON** TACO!

I WON'T BE **LONG**, JUST GO **ON** WITHOUT...

19

I WAS WONDERING IF YOU'D SHOW UP. I *ALMOST* MADE IT OUT OF THE *COUNTY* THIS TIME.

WELL, I GOT A *LATE* START. MRS. FOSTER DIDN'T NOTICE YOU WERE *MISSING* UNTIL AFTER DINNER.

AFTER DINNER? WELL THERE'S A *BIG* SURPRISE!

SO, TELL ME, WHAT WAS IT *THIS* TIME? THE *FOOD?* THE *DOG?* DIDN'T GET TO WATCH YOUR FAVORITE *TV SHOW?*

AW, IT'S A *PERFECT* HOME, SHERIFF.

REALLY.

IF YOU'RE A *CIRCUS FREAK!*

AND WHERE DO THEY KEEP FINDING THESE PEOPLE?! I MEAN, WHO EVER HEARD OF *FOSTER PARENTS* NAMED...

...FOSTER?!

SERIOUSLY, YOU CAN'T *MAKE* THIS STUFF UP!

THE FOSTER'S ARE **GOOD** PEOPLE. THERE AREN'T MANY FAMILIES WHO WOULD TAKE IN SO MANY KIDS.

I DOUBT YOU'D FIND A MUCH BETTER SITUATION.

SORRY SHERIFF, BUT **PRISON LIFE** ISN'T REALLY FOR ME.

I NEED MY **FREEDOM**...TO GET OUT AND SEE THINGS!

YOU'RE **TEN!**

THAT'S WHAT I **MEAN!**

I HAVE MY **WHOLE** LIFE AHEAD OF ME. I SHOULDN'T BE **WASTING** IT WITH A BUNCH OF **MISFITS** WHO DON'T EVEN KNOW ME!

BEING A BIT DRAMATIC, DON'T YOU THINK?

WE **ALL** NEED PEOPLE IN OUR LIVES.

I DON'T.

I DON'T NEED PEOPLE TELLING ME TO **COME** TO **BREAKFAST!** OR **GO** TO **SCHOOL!** OR YOU **TALK FUNNY!**

OR **THIS** SEAT IS TAKEN. OR WE ATE THE **LAST ONE.**

OR THERE'S NO ROOM FOR YOU.

24

WELL, IT SEEMS YOU KNOW WHAT YOU'RE *RUNNING FROM...* ANY IDEA WHAT YOU'RE *RUNNING TO?*

I DON'T KNOW, MAYBE *PARADISE.*

DON'T SUPPOSE YOU'LL EVER FIND PARADISE IF YOU'RE ALWAYS RUNNING AWAY FROM...

THAT'S *NOT* MY HOME!

AREN'T YOU *LISTENING?* I DON'T WANT TO *BE* THERE!

I'M NOT WHAT YOU'D CALL A *PEOPLE PERSON!* BESIDES, I KNOW WHAT A *FAMILY* LOOKS LIKE AND THAT'S *NOT* A FAMILY.

YOU KNOW, THERE ARE THINGS IN LIFE WE DON'T ALWAYS GET TO CHOOSE...

AND WHAT YOU NEED RIGHT NOW ARE PEOPLE WHO CAN TAKE CARE OF YOU... YOU NEED A *HOME.*

I CAN TAKE CARE OF MYSELF.

I'LL BE FINE.

=SIGH=

HEY!

WHAT?!

DON'T LEAN UP AGAINST THE CAR! YOU'LL SCRATCH THE PAINT!

IT'S JUST AN OLD POLICE CAR!

THIS IS NOT JUST ANY OLD CAR!

IT'S A NEW OLD CAR! A COLLECTIBLE!

A 1964 FORD GALAXIE 500. WITH A 250-HP THUNDERBIRD V-8, CRUISE-O-MATIC TRANSMISSION AND ONLY 42,000 ORIGINAL MILES.

FULLY RESTORED IN GLORIOUS BLACK AND WHITE! JUST LIKE THE ONE ANDY GRIFFITH DROVE DOWN THE STREETS OF MAYBERRY.

BEFORE BARNEY LEFT AND ANDY BECAME BITTER AND IRRITATED ALL THE TIME.

MY GRANDMOTHER DROVE A CAR EXACTLY LIKE THAT.

THIS IS NOT YOUR GRANDMOTHER'S CAR.

NO, REALLY, THAT'S HER CAR!

SHUT UP AND GET IN!

WELL, I *IMAGINE* YOU'LL BE TAKING ME TO A *NEW* HOME NOW.

I JUST HOPE THE *FOOD* IS *BETTER* THAN OL' LADY FOSTER'S.

AND MAYBE YOU CAN *CALL* AHEAD AND LET THEM KNOW I *SKIPPED* DINNER.

HOLD ON THERE HOSS, YOU'RE *NOT* GOING TO ANOTHER HOME.

WHAT DO YOU MEAN?

SORRY, RED, BUT YOU'VE PULLED THIS *STUNT* ONE TOO MANY TIMES. STRIKE THREE AND YOU'RE *OUT*. THEY'LL BE SENDING YOU TO A *FACILITY* NOW.

A *FACILITY*?! WHAT *FACILITY*?!

A HOME FOR KIDS. *TROUBLED KIDS*, LIKE YOU.

BUT I'M NOT TROUBLED... I'M JUST A LITTLE BIT OF A *CHALLENGE*.

THERE'S NOTHING I CAN DO, RED. IT'S THE LAW.

WHAT DO YOU MEAN, *THE LAW?!* I THOUGHT *YOU* WERE THE *LAW!*

AND *DON'T* CALL ME *RED!*

DEPUTY ONE TO SHERIFF RAMSEY!

THIS IS DEPUTY ONE TO SHERIFF RAMSEY! COME IN SHERIFF!

RAMSEY HERE, DEPUTY ONE. I **FOUND** THE GIRL...LOOKS LIKE WE'LL MAKE IT HOME **EARLIER** THAN WE THOUGHT.

SHERIFF! I'M IN HOT PURSUIT! **HOT PURSUIT!**

CALM DOWN THERE, JOSH. NOW **WHAT** EXACTLY ARE YOU IN *"HOT PURSUIT"* OF?

YOU KNOW THOSE **HOTRODS** THAT HAVE BEEN STREET RACING THROUGH MANCHESTER? WELL, LOOKS LIKE WE GOT US **ONE**, SHERIFF!

HOLY SMOKES! WELL, IT LOOKS LIKE I'M JUST ABOUT DONE HERE IF YOU NEED ANY **ASSISTANCE.**

WHAT'S YOUR 20?

ZOOOOSHHHH

30

HOLY SMOKES!

HEY, WHAT KIND OF COP CAR *IS* THIS? THERE'S **NO DOOR HANDLE?**

SLAM

DON'T YOU WORRY ABOUT THE HANDLE! JUST **STAY** PUT!

BUT I WANNA **SEE** WHAT IT IS!

UNGH!

FWUMP
FWUMP

YEP. LOOKS LIKE ONE OF YOUR **TYPICAL** UFOs, CONSISTING OF A DISC-SHAPED **SAUCER** WITH **MULTI-COLORED** LIGHTS.

HOW...?

I'VE SEEN THIS KIND OF THING BEFORE.

SUCH A CLICHÉ.

WHAT'S THAT **CRAZY** THING DOING?

I THINK IT'S **FREESTYLING**.

ENGH!

HMPH!

WELL, I THINK THE SHOW'S OVER...

LOOKS LIKE IT'S TAKING OFF.

THINK WE SHOULD *CALL* SOMEONE?

WHAT? LIKE THE *MILITARY*? THEY'D *NEVER* BELIEVE US.

YEAH, GUESS YOU'RE RIGHT...

I BETTER GET BACK— GOTTA GET THAT *CAR WASHED* BEFORE THAT *MUD* DRIES!

HEY...I THINK IT'S *COMING BACK!*

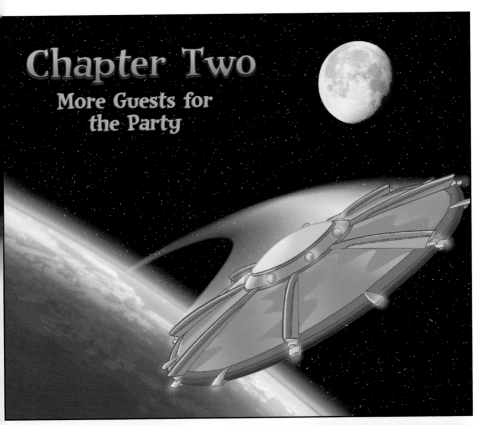

Chapter Two
More Guests for the Party

WE HAVE TO MAKE SURE EVERYTHING IS *PERFECT*.

I HAD TO PULL A LOT OF *STRINGS* TO GET US HERE...

THE *WORD* IS THESE GUYS WILL PAY *BIG BAZOOKS* FOR RARE AND EXOTIC *STUFF*!

HEY, THAT GUY LOOKS *IMPORTANT*!

GET OVER THERE AND TAKE CARE OF HIM! AND *DON'T* SCREW IT UP, EITHER!

I MUST SAY, YOUR PRODUCE LOOKS VERY *ENTICING*. BUT I FIND THAT I AM AT A DISADVANTAGE AS I AM *UNFAMILIAR* WITH THESE *SPECIES*.

WHAT WOULD YOU *RECOMMEND* TO THE *UNINITIATED*?

OOO. IT APPEARS TO BE SOME VARIETY OF... *PEAR*?

MAY I SAMPLE?

MMMM. QUITE EXTRAORDIN—

PLUNFH!

WHAT WERE YOU THINKING?!

YOU DON'T GIVE A **PUCKER-FRUIT** TO A **BLOVISHIAN!**

GREETINGS—I AM FIRST EXECUTIVE OFFICER, *FE*-05251977.

PLEASE STATE YOUR NAME AND PLANET OF ORIGIN.

HUH? OH, A LADY ROBOT.

YES MA'AM—I'M **CHAWEE** AND THIS IS MY FARMHAND, **TAWEE**, FROM THE PLANET CAWAWEE.

MAY I HAVE YOUR INVITATION, PLEASE?

MY, UH... INVITATION...YEAH, ABOUT THAT...

AUTHORIZATION IS REQUIRED TO PRESENT TO THEIR EXCELLENCIES, THE **AQUILARI**.

AUTHORIZATION? WE'RE JUST **FARMERS**—YOU KNOW, THE KIND YOU USUALLY SEE PARKED ON THE SIDE OF AN **ASTEROID**.

I'M SORRY, THE AQUILARI ARE ONLY INTERESTED IN THE RARE AND UNUSUAL, NOT THE **MUNDANE**.

OH, BUT WE **HAVE** THE *RARE* AND *UNUSUAL!*

I HAVE CAWAWEEAN PEACHES, LOQUATS, DEW-MAWS, JACKFRUIT, AND PURPLE DOZOONS! NOT TO MENTION...

...TWO RARE AND EXOTIC POTATOES!

POTATOES ARE THE SECOND MOST COMMON LIFE-FORM IN THE GALAXY.

BUM-BA-ROOOO

THEY HAVE ARRIVED!

M-BA-BUM-BA-RUOOOO

LADIES AND GENTLEMEN, VISITORS FROM **ALL WORLDS**, I PRESENT TO YOU... THE ANCIENTS OF CHELONIA, COLLECTORS OF TIME, THE LAST SAGES OF THE WANDERING, THEIR EXCELLENCIES...

THE **AQUILARI!**

EXCEPT FOR TWO UNINVITED POTATO FARMERS, EVERYTHING IS IN ORDER, YOUR EXCELLENCIES. I THINK YOU WILL BE PLEASED.

IF YOU ACT **NOW**, I'LL THROW IN...

...THIS **BEAUTIFUL** FREE-RANGE *PERSONAL ASSISTANT* TO REPLACE YOUR CROCKPOT THERE!

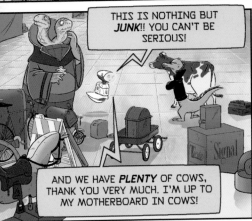

THIS IS NOTHING BUT **JUNK**!! YOU CAN'T BE SERIOUS!

AND WE HAVE **PLENTY** OF COWS, THANK YOU VERY MUCH. I'M UP TO MY MOTHERBOARD IN COWS!

NOW YOU'RE JUST BEING **SILLY**.

YOU CAN **NEVER** HAVE ENOUGH COWS.

OOOOOOOO

OH, WHAT'S THIS? DID A LITTLE TREASURE CATCH YOUR EYE?

AH, A **PERFECT** CHOICE FOR THE GIANT TWO-HEADED TURTLE WHO HAS **EVERYTHING**.

49

AH...YES. A **CLASSIC** INDEED. A **PRIMITIVE** COMBUSTIBLE, UH, MACHINE...ALLOY CONSTRUCTION...

AN **AUTHORITARIAN** VEHICLE...IN, UH, TRADITIONAL **FESTIVE** COLORS...

BUT **DON'T** LET ME BORE YOU WITH THE **DETAILS!**

WAIT TILL YOU **HEAR** THAT ENGINE!

IT PURRS LIKE A **HUNGRY** KITTEN.

THIEVES!

IT'S JUST A *MISUNDERSTANDING*. THEIR EXCELLENCIES ARE *NOT*... HMPH!

CAN YOU MAKE OUT *WHAT* HE WANTS?

THE *TRANSLATOR* CAN'T QUITE GET A LOCK ON IT— THE BEST IT CAN COME UP WITH IS *"TREASURE"*?

YOUR EXCELLENCIES!

IT SEEMS WE HAVE MORE GUESTS FOR THE *PARTY*.

USKOG *PIRATES?*

RETURN NOW! USKOG MAKE *FORCE!*

BUT THEY'RE JUST A *MYTH*—AN OLD FOLK TALE.

YET, *THERE* THEY ARE...

AND THEY *INSIST* WE HAVE SOMETHING THAT *BELONGS* TO *THEM*.

WE HAVE ACQUIRED *NOTHING* THAT IS NOT IN THE *PUBLIC DOMAIN*.

IF YOU THINK *YOU* CAN *CONVINCE* THEM, THEN BY ALL MEANS...

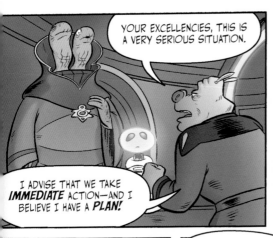

YOUR EXCELLENCIES, THIS IS A VERY SERIOUS SITUATION.

I ADVISE THAT WE TAKE **IMMEDIATE** ACTION—AND I BELIEVE I HAVE A **PLAN!**

IF WE CAN **CLEAR** THE SURROUNDING **MERCHANT VESSELS** WE SHOULD BE ABLE TO MAKE THE **JUMP** TO **LIGHT SPEED**—THE USKOG WILL BE UNABLE TO **TRACK** US.

THE AQUILARI TRUST YOUR JUDGEMENT, CAPTAIN.

DO WHAT YOU MUST TO SAVE THE SHIP.

HELM! PREPARE TO **WEIGH ANCHOR.**

RELEASE DAMPERS! SET STARBOARD SHIELDS FOR **MAXIMUM FORCE!**

BUCKLE UP EVERYONE.

ON MY COMMAND.

FULL POWER!

HARD TO PORT!

"CAPTAIN, THE *USKOG* ARE STILL UNABLE TO GET A *CLEAR SHOT*."

MAINTAIN *FULL* POWER TO DORSAL *SHIELDS!* KEEP THOSE BAY DOORS *CLEAR!*

THE MERCHANTS WILL CREATE A *BARRIER* BETWEEN US AND THE *USKOG.*

WHAT'S THE *DISTANCE* TO THE LAUNCH ZONE?

20 KILOMETERS AND CLOSING.

BEGIN THE *CALCULATIONS* FOR *HYPERSPACE.*

"THE PIRATES HAVE *CLEARED* THE BARRIER AND ARE *POWERING WEAPONS!*"

"CALCULATIONS COMPLETE—WE ARE ENTERING *LAUNCH ZONE.*"

MAKE THE JUMP NOW!

WHAT IS THAT?!

A *HIT* TO OUR STARBOARD ENGINES AT THE PRECISE MOMENT OF *JUMP*!

ENGINE CONTAINMENT *CRITICAL*...

LOSING *HYPERDRIVES* FOUR AND FIVE...

...*PLASMA LEAK* ON STARBOARD ENGINE!

...*UNABLE* TO MAINTAIN *LIGHT VELOCITY*!

I WANT *ALL POWER* TO *SUB-LIGHT* ENGINES...

AND *BRACE* YOURSELVES FOR HARD *DECELERATION*!

IT'S GONNA GET *BUMPY*!

HELM, WHERE **ARE** WE?

UNKNOWN, CAPTAIN.

ALL SYSTEMS ARE **OFF-LINE!**

REROUTE **ALL** POWER TO **EMERGENCY** SYSTEMS.

WE'RE BEING **PULLED** IN BY THE PLANET'S GRAVITY! WE'RE **DRIFTING** TOWARD THE **PLANET'S RING!**

YOUR EXCELLENCIES, I'M AFRAID WE'VE **RUN OUT** OF **OPTIONS.**

AT THIS RATE, THE SHIP WILL BE **PULLED** INTO THE PLANET'S RING BEFORE WE REGAIN CONTROL!

WE COULD TRY TO **REBOOT** THE SHIP'S SYSTEMS, BUT EVEN **IF** WE SUCCEED, THE **CHANCES** OF A **SAFE LANDING** ARE **MINIMAL.**

WE **MUST** MOVE TO **SAFETY.**

IT...IS...

...TIME...

THANK YOU, YOUR EXCELLENCIES...

ALL HANDS, *THIS* IS THE *CAPTAIN* SPEAKING...

PROCEED DIRECTLY TO YOUR ASSIGNED *SHUTTLECRAFT!*

THIS IS *NOT* A DRILL!

I REPEAT, THIS IS *NOT A DRILL*—

ABANDON SHIP!

ONCE YOU HAVE CLEARED THE SHIP, I WILL ENGAGE THE **EMERGENCY** PROTOCOL.

IF I AM **SUCCESSFUL**, I WILL SECURE THE SHIP, SET A **BEACON**, AND AWAIT YOUR RETURN.

YOUR LIFE-PODS HAVE **LIMITED** PROPULSION...

...SO YOU MAY NOT BE ABLE TO **RETURN** FOR SOME TIME.

IS THERE ANYTHING ELSE, YOUR EXCELLENCIES?

PROTECT...THE... COLLECTION..

GOODBYE, YOUR EXCELLENCIES.

LEAVE ME ALONE!

WHAT DO YOU WANT?!

HEY! GET THAT THING AWAY FROM ME!

OW! HEY!

FEELING THE EFFECT OF THE *GIBBERVOX* NOW.

HUH?

I *SAID*, YOU SHOULD *EXPECT* TO UNDERSTAND EVERYONE NOW.

UNLESS, YOU DON'T HAVE THE *CAPACITY* FOR *LANGUAGE*.

THE TRANSLATION FOR *"GRUNT"* IS STILL *"GRUNT."*

WAIT! I JUST UNDERSTOOD *EVERYTHING* YOU SAID!

YEESSSSS?

AND YOU'RE *ALIENS!*

WELL, *YOU'RE* NOT... YOU'RE A ROBOT...

...WELL, YOU MIGHT BE AN *ALIEN* ROBOT, BUT...

OOOH, THIS IS SO *AWESOME!*

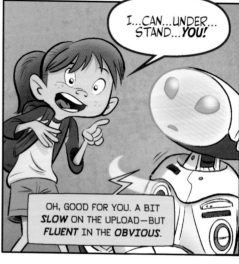

I...CAN...UNDER... STAND...*YOU!*

OH, GOOD FOR YOU. A BIT *SLOW* ON THE UPLOAD—BUT *FLUENT* IN THE *OBVIOUS.*

ALL RIGHT!
DON'T PANIC!

EVERYTHING IS GOING TO BE JUST FINE, SON—DON'T YOU WORRY. WHAT WE *NEED* IS A *PLAN* OF *ACTION*.

IT WILL BE *DARK* SOON, AND I IMAGINE THE TEMPERATURE WILL DROP...

...SO FIRST, WE SHOULD BUILD A *FIRE* AND MAKE A *SHELTER*.

MOST OF ALL, WE NEED TO STAY *POSITIVE*.

ARE YOU *WITH* ME?

C'MON, STU!

WE SHOULDN'T GET TOO FRIENDLY UNTIL WE KNOW WHO THESE *CREATURES* ARE AND WHAT THEY WANT.

MAN, I'VE GOTTA *STOP* DOING THAT HAND THING.

WOW!

WATCHIT!

AHHHHH!

SORRY!

OOPS!

YOU'D THINK WITH *THAT* MANY *EYES* IT'D *SEE* WHERE IT WAS *GOIN'*.

S'MONOFTH EMMEMNLLO MONMON...

...YUP!

A *BIG-EYED GRAY* ALIEN! YIPES! THEY GIVES ME THE *CREEPS!*

I'VE HEARD ABOUT *THOSE* GUYS—THEY'RE *NEVER* UP TO ANY GOOD!

I BET *YOU* KNOW WHAT'S GOING ON AROUND HERE, DON'TCHA, *BIG EYES?*

HUH? WHAT DO YOU HAVE TO SAY FOR *YOURSELF?*

YA' KNOW, I DON'T THINK THE GUY KNOWS *ANYTHING.*

NO...

HE KNOWS *SOMETHING.*

NO, REALLY! *LOOK...* IS *THIS* THE FACE OF SOMEONE WHO *KNOWS* SOMETHING?

MAYBE WE SHOULD LEAVE HIM *ALONE.*

YEAH? WELL, MAYBE *YOU* SHOULD *MIND* YOUR OWN *BUSINESS!*

YEAH! YOU HEARD HIM, *RED!*

WHAT...

...DID...

...YOU...

...SAY?

85

PLEASE! *PLEASE!* *WHAT* IS GOING ON?

WE CAUGHT ONE OF THOSE *GRAYS!* YOU KNOW, WITH THE *EYES,* AND THE *PROBES,* AND THE...UH...

WELL, JUST *LOOK* AT HIM!

AND IT'S GOT A *TASTY* TREAT!

GRAY? HE'S JUST A FRUIT FARMER...MR. *TAWEE,* AS I RECALL—AND, EVIDENTLY, HE *MISSED* HIS FLIGHT.

JUST PUT HIM *DOWN* AND TRY TO *PLAY NICE.*

SEE? *NOTHING* TO GET EXCITED ABOUT.

NOW, *THAT* IS TAKEN CARE OF...

HEY!

YOU KEEP *ZIPPING* AROUND HERE LIKE YOU *OWN* THE PLACE!

I THINK YOU KNOW *MORE* THAN YOU'RE SAYING! SO...

HOW ABOUT COMING BACK HERE AND GIVING *US* SOME *ANSWERS!*

YEAH! LIKE WHERE *ARE* WE?

AND *HOW* DID WE GET HERE?

C'MON, *SPEAK UP!*

WELL? HOW 'BOUT IT?

WAIT! *WAIT!* ONE AT A *TIME!*

LET'S SEE... MECHANICAL *MISHAP*, CREW *EVACUATED*, SHIP *CRASHED*.

NOW, IF YOU WILL *EXCUSE* ME...

HEY! WAIT JUST A MINUTE!

HOW ABOUT EXPLAINING HOW I ENDED UP ON THAT *"SHIP"* IN THE *FIRST* PLACE!

I DON'T REMEMBER *EVER* SEEING ANYTHING LIKE THAT THING, NEVER MIND GETTING *ON* IT.

ME *NEITHER!* I WON'T EVEN GET ON AN *ESCALATOR*.

PFFFT! I DON'T EVEN *BELIEVE* IN SPACE-SHIPS!

LAST THING *I* REMEMBER WAS FLOSSING MY TEETH, THEN *BAM!* DESERT HOLIDAY!

HEY, THERE WOULDN'T BE A *BATHROOM* ON YOUR SPACESHIP, WOULD THERE?

I GOTTA TALK TO A MAN ABOUT A *GORG*.

I HAVE NO DATA ON HOW YOU *BEGAN* YOUR JOURNEYS—ALL I KNOW IS, WE WERE ATTACKED BY *PIRATES* AND *CRASHED*.

PIRATES?! DID SHE SAY PIRATES?!

THAT'S SO *AWESOME!*

YOU KNOW WHAT *I* THINK. I THINK *YOU* AND THE LITTLE GRAY GUY *HIJACKED* US!

YOU MEAN "KIDNAPPED."

KIDNAPPED US!

YOU ABDUCTED US?!

MY MASTERS DID NOT *ABDUCT* ANYONE.

I KNEW THEM *SAUCERS* WAS OUT THERE! I TOLD LOVELLE HERE! I SAID, "*BABY*, THEM *SAUCERS* IS OUT THERE."

MMM*YUP!*

SO WHERE DID WE CRASH? *LOOKS* LIKE TEXAS. IS IT *TEXAS*?

THIS *PLANET* ISN'T IN MY DATABANKS.

BUT IT IS ONLY A MATTER OF TIME BEFORE MY MASTERS FIND US AND *RETURN*.

JUST WHO ARE THESE "*MASTERS*" YOU KEEP TALKING ABOUT?

YOU AREN'T IN SOME KIND OF CREEPY *ROBOT CULT*, ARE YOU?

I MEAN, MAYBE YOU JUST WANT TO KEEP US HERE UNTIL THEY *RETURN* TO EAT OUR *BRAINS*!

BRAINS?

AWESOME!

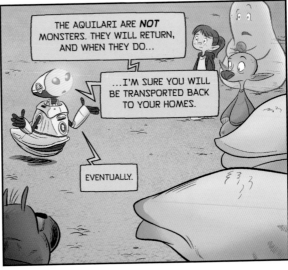

THE AQUILARI ARE *NOT* MONSTERS. THEY WILL RETURN, AND WHEN THEY DO...

...I'M SURE YOU WILL BE TRANSPORTED BACK TO YOUR HOMES.

EVENTUALLY.

WHAT DO YOU MEAN *EVENTUALLY?*

WELL, IT MAY TAKE SOME *TIME* FOR THEM TO LOCATE OUR *BEACON.*

GIVEN OUR DISTANCE FROM OTHER INHABITED SYSTEMS, THE MAGNETIC INTERFERENCE FROM THE PLANET'S POLES OR NEARBY PLANETARY BODIES...

GET TO IT, *SCRAP HEAP!*

ONE TO THREE *YEARS*!

WHAT!?

PLEASE! PLEASE! KEEP IN MIND, WHEN I SAY "YEARS" I MEAN *RELATIVE* TO THIS PLANET.

PLANETS, OF COURSE, *REVOLVE* AROUND THEIR SUNS AT *DIFFERENT RATES*...

I THINK SHE'S MAKING *THAT* PART UP!

AND THE *DAY* HERE IS *SHORTER* THAN THE AVERAGE PLANET.

WAIT, HOW MANY *DAYS* IN A YEAR?

714.

I DON'T KNOW **WHAT** THIS IS, BUT I HOPE IT **BURNS**.

YOU SEE HOW IMPORTANT **SURVIVAL SKILLS** ARE, STUIE?

GOOD JOB, DAD. MAYBE YOU CAN WHIP UP SOME **CAMPFIRE TREATS** WHILE YOU'RE AT IT.

HELLO.

MAY I SHARE YOUR FIRE?

OH!

I...UH...GUESS THAT WOULD BE OKAY.

YOU'RE QUITE THE INTERPLANETARY **OUTDOORSMAN**.

OH, YEAH...THE FIRE. HA HA.

IS EVERYTHING ALL RIGHT?

UH... **SURE**... WHY?

YOU'RE **STARING** AT ME.

I **AM**?

OH. SORRY. I WAS ONLY...WELL...

IT'S JUST...YOU'RE SO **DIFFERENT**...

...FROM **US**.

I MEAN...

I IMAGINE OUR WORLDS AREN'T SO DIFFERENT.

IN THEORY, **INTELLIGENT** LIFE COULD DEVELOP FROM ANY NUMBER OF SPECIES—REPTILES, RODENTS, FISH...

PINEAPPLE?

MAYBE EVEN PINEAPPLE.

MY NAME IS DELL.

GENE. I'M GENE, AND THIS IS STU.

HELLO, STU.

HI.

I CAN'T BELIEVE THIS IS **REALLY** HAPPENING!

WHAT A **MISERABLE** PARENT I TURNED OUT TO BE! I CAN'T EVEN TAKE MY KID OUT **CAMPING** AND **FISHING** WITHOUT GETTING **ABDUCTED** BY ALIENS!

YOU REALLY SHOULDN'T BE SO HARD ON YOURSELF.

IT'S NOT EASY BEING A SINGLE PARENT ON A **NORMAL** DAY, BUT YOU **NEVER** EXPECT **THIS** KIND OF THING TO HAPPEN!

I DON'T EVEN **BELIEVE** IN... "EXTRATERRESTRIALS"?

ISN'T THAT WHAT YOU CALL THEM?

IT'S ALL SO... **ALIEN.**

AND WHAT DO WE HAVE HERE?

A TASTY EGG, MAXX! A VERY *SHINY* TASTY EGG!

SO TELL ME, GRAY-BOY...

...WHAT'S IN THE EGG?

MOMMY PACK YOU A *LUNCH?*

PLACLUNK

HEH?

LOOKY THERE, BAZIL, IT'S LITTLE *BIG MOUTH!*

OOPS.

AND LOOKS LIKE *IT* HAS SOMETHING TASTY *TOO.*

I HOPE YOU BROUGHT ENOUGH TO *SHARE,* RED...

HEY! THAT'S *MINE!*

THERE *ISN'T* ANY MORE "MINE"...

...WE'RE ALL JUST ONE *BIG HAPPY FAMILY* NOW!

SNAP

OOMF!

AAAAAHHHHHHHHHHHHHHHHHHHHHH!

FHUMP

UNGH!

HEY! THEY TOOK MY **SHOE!**

WHO TAKES **ONE** SHOE?!

A **LIZARD?** AND A GUY WITH **OCTOPUS LEGS?!** WHAT DO **THEY** NEED WITH A **SHOE?!**

DID YOU **HEAR** ME?! **ONE** OF THOSE **GUYS** DIDN'T EVEN **HAVE FEET!!**

WHAT'S **WRONG** WITH THIS PLACE?!

ON **MY** PLANET, NO ONE STEALS JUST **ONE** SHOE!

ALIENS ARE BAD, **BAD** PEOPLE.

THAT'S *IT!* I'M *DONE!* *OUTTA* HERE!

I'VE GOT FOOD, WATER...

THERE ARE A FEW CLOUDS OVER THOSE MOUNTAINS.

I'M NOT SO GOOD AT ALIEN SCIENCE...BUT THAT *COULD* MEAN RAIN.

AND IF THERE'S RAIN MAYBE THERE'S *SOMETHING* GREEN. BUT IT DOESN'T MATTER...

I JUST *DON'T* WANT TO BE HERE ANYMORE.

WHOA, WHOA, WHOA!

WHERE DO THINK *YOU'RE* GOING, *EGG-BOY?*

YOU'RE *NOT* COMING WITH *ME!*

GO MAKE *FRIENDS* SOMEWHERE ELSE!

SO, YOUR NAME IS TAWEE, HUH?

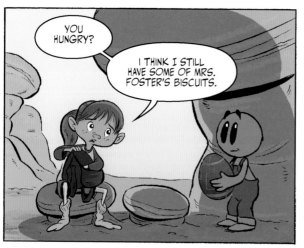

YOU HUNGRY?

I THINK I STILL HAVE SOME OF MRS. FOSTER'S BISCUITS.

I'M NOT SURE IF THEY SURVIVED TRAVELING ACROSS THE *GALAXY* AND *CRASHING* ON A DESERTED PLANET...

BUT THEY CAN'T BE ANY WORSE THAN WHEN SHE TOOK THEM OUT OF THE OVEN.

HEY, DID YOUR *EYES* JUST GET *BIGGER*?

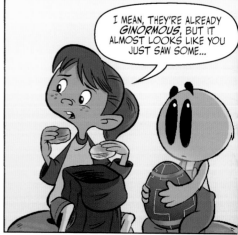

I MEAN, THEY'RE ALREADY *GINORMOUS*, BUT IT ALMOST LOOKS LIKE YOU JUST SAW SOME...

OH BOY.

IF YOU HAVE *ANY* IDEAS, THIS WOULD BE A GREAT TIME FOR YOU TO START *TALKING.*

AAAACK!

AHHHHHHH*RUN!*

116

OH, NO. **BOBALUNX!**

YOU DIDN'T GO AND *FEED* THEM, DID YOU? YOU *NEVER* FEED A BOBALUNX.

HOW WOULD *I* KNOW THAT?!

EVERYONE KNOWS THAT! YOU'D HAVE TO LIVE ON THE OTHER SIDE OF THE *GALAXY* TO MISS THAT ONE!

IS THAT SO?!

WELL, YOU'RE SUCH AN *EXPERT*, WHY DON'T YOU TELL ME WHAT *"EVERYONE"* WOULD DO *NOW*?

EH...

I HAVE *NO IDEA* WHAT *"EVERYONE"* WOULD DO...

BUT I'D START... *RUNNING!*

THAT'S WHAT I *WAS* DOING!

TAWEE?

RUN, TAWEE, *RUN!*

LOOK, I KNOW WHAT YOU'RE THINKING...

HOW CAN WE LEAVE THAT GUY DOWN THERE WITH A BUNCH OF **HUNGRY** BLUE FROG THINGYS?

AND MY QUESTION TO **YOU** WOULD BE, WHAT CAN A POCKET-SIZED ALIEN WITH HIS HANDS FULL AND A **KID** DO?

BESIDES, I DON'T THINK MR. GRUMPY PUSS...

...WANTS...ANY ...HELP.

WHOA...

I THINK WE STUMBLED INTO SOME KINDA PARADISE.

HELLO?

ANYBODY HOME?

HMM, THIS **KINDA** LOOKS LIKE **EARTH** STUFF...

BUT IT DOESN'T LOOK LIKE ANYONE'S BEEN HERE IN A **LONG** TIME.

UGH!

MAKE THAT A **VERY** LONG TIME!

HEY!

WHAT ARE YOU **DOING?!**

YOU CAN'T BE **THERE!** WHAT IF SOMEONE **DOES** LIVE HERE!

AND WHAT IF THAT SOMEONE IS AN **IT!**

WHAT IF "**IT**" IS A **GIANT CYPLOPS** WHO'S JUST A BIG **SLOB** AND THIS ISN'T AN **ABANDONED** SHACK AFTER ALL!

AND WHAT IF "**IT**" WALKS THROUGH THAT DOOR WANTING AN **EGG** AND **ALIEN** DINNER!

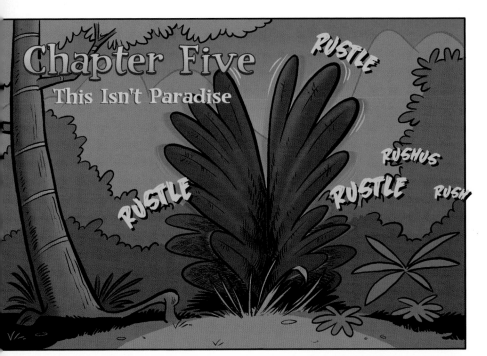

Chapter Five
This Isn't Paradise

GLIBX

YOU **STILL** HERE?

I THOUGHT YOU'D BE **LONG GONE** BY NOW!

WELL, I'M GLAD YOU'RE AWAKE, BECAUSE I **DIDN'T** GET A CHANCE TO TELL YOU SOMETHING LAST NIGHT...

GO AWAY!

SLAM

UHHHG.

SLAM

YA KNOW, I'VE BEEN LOOKING THROUGH **BOOKS** 'N' **CHARTS** ALL MORNING AND CAN'T SEEM TO FIND A SPECIES LIKE YOU ANYWHERE **ON** THIS PLANET.

NOW **WHY** DO YOU SUPPOSE THAT IS?

WELL...

MAYBE IT'S BECAUSE...

...AHM NOT FWOM AWOUND HERW.

YA DON'T SAY?

WHU-HUH!

WELL, I HOPE YOU KNOW, **YOU'RE** IN A LOT OF TROUBLE.

WHAT? ARE YOU LIKE A **SHERIFF** OR SOMETHING?

SHERIFF?...

YOU WANT TO KNOW WHO **I** AM? **I'M** THE CAT WHO LOOKS AFTER THIS PLACE!

THAT'S WHO I AM!

AND **I** MAKE SURE SMART-MOUTHED MONKEYS LIKE **YOU** DON'T SCARE THE FISH OR SLEEP IN MY BED!

THIS IS A PROTECTED PLANET! AND **YOU** BEING HERE MEANS **LOTS** OF EXTRA WORK FOR ME!

SO, WHEN YOU'RE **FINISHED** WITH YOUR BREAKFAST, IT'S TIME FOR **YOU** TO...

WAIT, SO YOU'RE LIKE A **PARK RANGER?**

YES.

NO!

YOU KNOW WHAT? **I** ASK THE QUESTIONS AROUND HERE! LIKE...

HOW'D **YOU** GET HERE?

GWIANT PACESHWIP.

A **GIANT** SPACESHIP, HUH...

UN, HUH! **REALLY** BIG ONE.

AS **BIG** AS A **CITY!** THERE I WAS—SLEEPING IN THE BACK SEAT OF THE POLICE CAR.

THEN, SUDDENLY, IT **CRASHED** IN THE DESERT.

THE POLICE CAR?

THE SPACESHIP.

AND THERE WERE **ALL** THOSE ALIENS...

AYE YAI YAI!

THERE WAS THE GRAY ONE WITH THE BIG EYES, WHO'S NAMED **TAWEE**...

AND THE **ROBOT**...

THE MEAN ONE...

THE LITTLE LIZARD

THE LADY LIZARD

THE PLANTS

THE FUZZY ONES

THE JELLO ONES

THE ONE-EYED ONES

HEY! ARE YOU LISTENING?!

LISTENING?! I CAN'T HEAR ANYTHING **BUT** YOUR BABBLING!

AND...I DON'T BELIEVE A **WORD** OF IT!

IF A SHIP **THAT** BIG CRASHED SO CLOSE, I **THINK** I WOULD HAVE HEARD IT.

WELL, MAYBE YOU **SLEPT** THROUGH IT.

SLEPT THROUGH IT?

OKAY! FIRST, THERE'D BE A **BIG** NOISE.

NEXT, THE GROUND WOULD **SHAKE**...**ALARMS** WOULD GO OFF...

HOW COULD I **MISS** SOMETHING LIKE **THAT**?

T! **BLERT! BLERT! BLERT!**

BAM

WELL...WHAT WAS **THAT**?

NOTHING.

FINE! I'LL **SHOW** YOU!

IT'S JUST THIS **THING**... THE **BEEPY** THING!! IT'S TECHNICAL... YOU WOULDN'T UNDERSTAND!

AND IT **BEEPS!** FOR **NO** PARTICULAR REASON...

...IT DOESN'T MEAN A GIANT SPACESHIP CRASHED! IT JUST **BEEPS!**

IT'S A **COMPUTER?**

WHAT ARE **YOU** DOING WITH A **COMPUTER?!**

HEY! DO YOU PLAY VIDEO **GAMES?** LIKE **MIME-SHAFT?**

OR **SUPER MUSTACHIOS!** I **LOVE** THAT GAME!

SUSHHHH!

OK...WHY ISN'T THIS WORKING?

DID YOU TURN IT ON?!

YES! I TURNED IT ON!

WAIT...MAYBE... AH, OKAY...

THERE IT GOES!

BLOO

YEAH, I CAN SEE HOW YOU'D **MISS** THAT.

MMMMM.

SLURP

HEY! DON'T BE A SORE LOSER. YOU DON'T **HAVE** TO LEAVE. YOU CAN **KEEP** THE HOUSE...

I'M NOT REALLY INTO **BAD SMELLS**...DO YOU EVER CHANGE THE **LITTER?**

YOU'RE **NOT** STAYING HERE!

I'M GLAD WE AGREE!

I'M THINKING THE **OTHER** SIDE OF THE VALLEY. A SMALL HUT... A HAMMOCK.

YOU KNOW? LIKE THOSE **PARADISE** POST CARDS?

YOU'LL **NEVER** KNOW I'M THERE. WE'LL JUST **WAVE** AT EACH OTHER ON **GARBAGE DAY.**

THAT'S **NOT** WHAT I MEAN!

YOU'RE GOING TO TAKE ME TO THAT **CRASH SITE!**

WHAT?! I JUST WALKED FOR **TWO** DAYS THROUGH THAT DESERT!

I'M **NOT** GOING BACK THERE!

TWO DAYS?! WHAT DID YOU DO, **WALK** IN **CIRCLES?**

IT'S ONLY HALF A DAY'S JOURNEY TO THOSE COORDINATES!

HOW WOULD **I** KNOW **THAT?**

HEY! CAN'T YOU **CARRY** ME?

NO!

WELL, THIS IS CHEERY.

NOT VERY MANY BEINGS FOR A SHIP SO BIG.

WHERE ARE ALL THE OTHERS?

HUH?

IT CAME BACK?

LOVELLE, WAKE UP!

THE *RED ONE*...WITH ALL THE CRAZY *EYES!*

IT CAME BACK! AND IT BROUGHT *SOMETHING* WITH IT!

HEY, LOOK EVERYONE!

IT CAME BACK!

THANK YOU! THANK YOU FOR COMING! WE'VE JUST BEEN LEFT HERE...ABANDONED!

YEAH, YEAH, HANG ON THERE SPARKY...

JUST WHO'S IN CHARGE HERE?

I GUESS YOU COULD SAY THAT CRAZY APPLIANCE IS IN CHARGE!

APPLIANCE?

HE MEANS THE ROBOT, FE-05...2... UH...SOMETHING. LOCKED HERSELF IN THE SPACESHIP.

SHE DONE GONE LOONEY! WE AIN'T SEEN HER IN DAYS!

WELL, HOW DO I GET IN THERE?

THERE'S A HATCH OVER THERE.

MY LITTLE ALFIE HAS GAS.

UH...

POP

WHO IS HE?

SOMEONE SAID HE'S SPECIAL FORCES.

I THINK HE'S JUST A MECHANIC.

NAW, HE'S DRESSED TOO NICE TO BE A MECHANIC.

ENNGH!

SO...HOW DO YOU GET IN THERE?

YOU CAN RING THE BUZZER...

BUT SHE WON'T OPEN IT.

BUZZER, EH?

WELL, I'LL JUST SEE ABOUT THAT.

OH! HELLO?

BUZZZZZ

HEY! OPEN UP IN THERE!

WHO...IS... THIS?

MY NAME IS...

THAT'S NOT IMPORTANT! I WANT TO TALK TO WHOEVER'S IN CHARGE!

THEY'RE HERE! WE'RE SAVED! ONE MOMENT, PLEASE!

HELLO! I AM FE-05251977...

OH!

ARE...ARE... YOU...ALONE?

UH...

WELL...

EXCEPT FOR *THESE* FINE FOLKS, YES. *YES*, I AM.

OH.

OH!

YOU MUST BE THE *FIRST RESPONDER!*

YES! OF COURSE! PLEASE COME IN! *COME IN!*

WOOF!

NOT YOU!

NOW THEN, WELCOME TO...

OH! WHERE DID SHE COME FROM?

DON'T WORRY, SHE'S WITH...

WAIT! DID YOU SAY...

SHE?!

YOU'RE A SHE?!

UH, YEA-UH! WHAT DIFFERENCE DOES IT MAKE?

IS THAT A TRICK QUESTION?

AND HOW WOULD YOU NOT KNOW?

ARE YOU READY?! IT'S TIME TO PLAY THE FAMILY FEUD!

WELL, ALIEN MONKEY GENDER ISN'T ONE OF MY AREAS OF EXPERTISE!

OH, MY... DID I SAY THAT OUT LOUD?

I DO BEG YOUR PARDON.

SEEMS I HAVE A LITTLE GLITCH...A FEW TOO MANY ROCKS TO THE HARDWARE, IF YOU KNOW WHAT I MEAN.

BUT I KNOW WHY YOU'RE HERE, SO IF YOU'RE READY...

ALL ABOARD! woooo...

THAT'S ONE ODD ROBOT.

SHE ALWAYS LIKE THAT?

NOPE. THIS IS ALL NEW.

HEY! FE... UH...FE... WHAT'S HER NAME AGAIN?

FE? EFFIE. OH, I LIKE THAT! CALL ME *EFFIE!*

HE JUST WANTS TO ASK YOU A FEW QUESTIONS.

QUESTIONS?

I LOVE QUESTIONS!

GREAT! WELL HERE'S A REALLY *FUN* ONE...

WHO EXACTLY *OWNS* THIS SHIP??

THE CHELDONIA IS THE PROPERTY OF THEIR EXCELLENCIES, THE AQUALARI.

WELL, YOUR *EXCELLENT* FRIENDS NEED TO MOVE THIS HUNK OF STARSHIP *ASAP!*

IT'S A BIT OF AN *EYESORE*...RUINS THE VIEW, IF YOU KNOW WHAT I MEAN.

YES, YES. WATCH YOUR STEP.

HEY, *I* HAVE A QUESTION...

WHERE ARE WE GOING?

UP.

YOU DON'T SAY...

I'M THINKING WE HAVE A SLIGHT *COMMUNICATION* PROBLEM HERE...

HA HA! I CAN'T BELIEVE IT! IT'S AN OLD *Z-93!*

I HAVEN'T SEEN ONE OF THOSE IN AGES!

I USED TO HAVE ONE WHEN I WAS A TEENAGER.

WAIT! YOU CAN FLY A *SPACESHIP?*

YOU CAN'T EVEN USE A *COMPUTER!*

SPACESHIP?! IT *ISN'T* A SPACESHIP!

THIS IS A FINELY TUNED *PRECISION* MACHINE! THE FINEST *HOV-ROD* EVER MADE.

WHAT IS UP WITH EVERYONE AND THEIR *STUPID* CAR LOVE?!

WHERE DID ALL THIS STUFF COME FROM?

DIFFERENT MEANS OF ACQUISITION.

DEALERS, ESTATE SALES, GIFTS, INTERNET AUCTIONS.

IT MUST BE WORTH...

I CAN'T GET MY HEAD AROUND IT.

THE COLLECTION IS PRICELESS.

AND IT IS MY DUTY TO KEEP IT SAFE UNTIL MY MASTERS RETURN.

HEY, WHAT'S *THAT* THING?!

OH, YES! THE MOST RECENT ACQUISITION.

WAIT! IT'S *REAL*?

I MEAN *REAL*-REAL. NOT *STUFFED*.

YOU COLLECT *REAL* THINGS.

YES, OF COURSE, JUST LOOK...

OH, SILLY ME. I FORGOT TO SWITCH ON THE LIGHTS.

CLAP CLAP

LIGHTS!

AS YOU CAN SEE, WE HAVE A *VAST* INVENTORY.

NEARLY EVERY *MODEL* THAT HAS EXISTED FOR, DARE I SAY, EONS.

SIR! SIR! WAIT! PLEASE!

ENGH!

YOU HAVEN'T SAID WHEN THE **FULL** RESCUE TEAM WILL ARRIVE.

AH...YEAH... WE'LL BE IN TOUCH.

HEY! CAN WE GET HOME NOW?

HOW LONG BEFORE WE LEAVE?

SO, DID YOU **FIX** IT?

NO! I DIDN'T "**FIX** IT"!

SEE? I TOLD YA.

HE'S JUST DRESSED TOO **NICE.**

BUT...WHERE'S HE GOING?

NOWHERE!

YOU! STOP FOLLOWING ME!

YOU CAN'T LEAVE ME HERE!

YES, I CAN! I'M GOING HOME. YOU...STAY!

BUT THOSE ALIEN COLLECTOR GUYS ARE GOING TO COME BACK!

AND THEY'RE GOING TO STUFF US AND STICK US ON A SHELF!

WHA...? WHO'S GOING TO STUFF WHO?!

AWESOME!

LOOK, IT'S **NONE** OF MY BUSINESS...

AND THE **LESS** I KNOW ABOUT ALL THIS, THE LESS **PAPERWORK** I HAVE TO FILL OUT.

AND THOSE GUYS **AREN'T** COMING BACK. YOU JUST STAY HERE WITH YOUR LITTLE FRIENDS...

...AND I'LL CALL A **TOW TRUCK**.

NO! I'M GOING WITH YOU.

NO! YOU'RE NOT!

WHY? IT'S **NOT YOUR** PLANET!

WAIT...**IS** IT YOUR PLANET?

YES. YES IT IS!

NO, IT **ISN'T!** **YOU** JUST MADE THAT UP!

FOR THE **LAST** TIME, **I'M** GOING WITH YOU!

FOR THE LAST TIME, YOU'RE **NOT** GOING WITH ME, **RED!**

HEY! LISTEN TO ME!

OVER THOSE MOUNTAINS, THERE IS A **VALLEY!** WITH **WATER!** AND **WEIRD-COLORED TREES!** AND PROBABLY WEIRD **ALIEN FRUIT!**

WHAT ARE YOU DOING?

AND **I** BET THERE'S ENOUGH FOR **EVERYONE!**

JUST FOLLOW **THAT** CAT IN THE **UGLY SHIRT** AND HE'LL LEAD YOU RIGHT TO IT!

WHA?!

FOOD?! AND WATER!?

NO!

WE'RE **SAVED!**

NO! STAY RIGHT THERE!

IS THIS **TRUE?**

EVERYONE! PLEASE! SETTLE DOWN!

JUST CALM DOWN!

THE LITTLE ONE WITH THE **LARGE MOUTH** DOESN'T KNOW WHAT SHE'S TALKING ABOUT.

THERE'S SOMETHING WRONG WITH HER...I'M THINKING SUN EXPOSURE.

UH...YOU KNOW, IT WAS PROBABLY JUST A **MIRAGE.** LITTLE TRICK OF... THE...LIGHT...

OK, **YES...** THERE **IS** A VALLEY...

BUT IT'S **TINY** AND I'M SURE THERE'S NOT ENOUGH ROOM FOR ALL YOU NICE...PEOPLE...TO BE **COMFORTABLE.**

MUCH TOO CROWDED...

I MEAN, LOOK AT **ALL** THIS OPEN **SPACE** YOU HAVE HERE.

OK! LOOK! I AM **NOT** TAKING ANY OF YOU WITH ME!

AND THAT'S THE **LAST** WORD!!

YOU'VE **GOT** TO BE KIDDING.

WE NEED TO WORK **TOGETHER!** BE A TEAM! NOW MOVE CLOSER... LIKE ONE **BIG ANIMAL!**

AND GET **LOUDER!**

REALLY LOUD! 1...2...3...

RAWRRR!

LOOK! THEY'RE RUNNING!

WE **DID** IT!

'CAUSE WE'RE **BIG** AND WE'RE **SCARY!**

NOPE...

IT'S BECAUSE **THAT'S** BIG AND SCARY!

YEAH! IT'S **RED'S** FAULT! **SHE** TALKED US INTO THIS!

WE **COULD** HAVE FOUND SHELTER AT THE **SHIP!**

ARE YOU **KIDDING?!**

I WAS JUST **TRYING** TO **HELP!**

YOU WERE TRYING TO HELP **YOURSELF!**

YEAH, HE WASN'T GOING TO SAY "**NO**" TO EVERYONE!

I DON'T THINK THERE EVEN **WAS** A VALLEY!

NO!

AND **NOW** WE'RE ALL **DOOMED!**

GET HER!

WHOA!

WAIT!

I HAVE AN *IDEA!*

EVERYONE **JUMP** INTO THE **HOLE!**

NICE TRY, RED! WE'RE NOT *THAT DUMB!*

YEAH! IF THIS IS SUCH A **GREAT** IDEA, THEN WHY DON'T *YOU...*

JUMP FIRST...

OKAY, WHO SAW *THAT* COMING?

IF I *SURVIVE* THIS...

I'M *SURE* I'LL REGRET IT!

WAIT!

ARE YOU *SURE* THERE ISN'T *ANOTHER*...

...WAY?

WELL, STU, IT'S KINDA OUT OF MY *COMFORT ZONE,* BUT WHAT DO YOU *SAY?!*

ARE YOU *WITH* ME?

YOU BET, DAD!

I'M WITH YOU *ALL* THE WAY!

ME TOO!

ALL RIGHT THEN...

WHAT'S GOING ON THERE, GOOSE? WHAT'S ALL THAT RACKET?

LEU, I'VE GOT A **REAL** PROBLEM HERE. A REAL **BIG** PROBLEM.

THERE ARE **ALIENS** HERE! **LOTS** OF ALIENS! **CASTAWAYS!** AND THE **BIGGEST** SHIP YOU'VE **EVER** SEEN.

YOU GOTTA COME HERE **NOW** AND **GET** THEM ALL! THEY'RE DRIVING ME **NUTS!**

CASTAWAYS? OK, OK... THERE'S A SUPPLY SHIP EN ROUTE TO A NEIGHBORING SYSTEM. THEY CAN BE THERE IN EIGHT WEEKS.

NO, NO, NO! YOU DON'T UNDERSTAND!

WHEN I TOOK THIS JOB, YOU **SAID** IF **ANYONE** EVER SHOWED UP, JUST CALL AND **YOU** WOULD TAKE CARE OF IT!

WELL, I'M **CALLING,** LEU! AND YOU HAVE TO COME AND GET THEM **NOW!**

IT'S LOW PRIORITY, GOOSE. THERE ARE OTHER THINGS THAT ARE JUST MORE IMPORTANT—LIKE TRYING TO FIGHT A WAR AGAINST PIRATES...

I JUST DON'T HAVE THE RESOURCES.

YOU TOLD ME THIS WOULD BE A **QUIET** JOB—**YOU** SAID IT WAS A **PARADISE!**

THIS ISN'T PARADISE!

I'M SORRY. YOU SHOULD HAVE PLENTY OF SUPPLIES TO SUPPORT EVERYONE UNTIL THEN. JUST MAKE THEM AS COMFORTABLE AS YOU CAN UNTIL HELP ARRIVES.

BUT, LEU...

IT'S THE BEST I CAN DO, GOOSE.

PLANET COMMAND OUT.

YOUR NAME IS *GOOSE*?

IT'S A *NICKNAME*... I GOT IT IN COLLEGE.

IT'S *COOL*.

ON *MY* PLANET, A GOOSE IS AN ANNOYING BIRD THAT *HONKS* ALL THE TIME.

HONK! HONK! **HONK!**

OUT! GET OUT!

WAIT A MINUTE...

YOU WENT TO *COLLEGE*?!

OUT! THIS IS *MY* HOUSE! THESE ARE *MY* THINGS!

YOU HEARD YOUR BOSS! YOU'RE SUPPOSED TO *SHARE* YOUR SUPPLIES UNTIL HELP COMES.

MINE! *MINE, MINE, MINE!*

WHERE ARE WE GOING TO *SLEEP?* WHAT ARE WE SUPPOSED TO *EAT?*

OUT THERE! BUILD YOUR *OWN* HOUSES!

THERE ARE *TREES* AND THERE ARE *THINGS* THAT *HANG* FROM THOSE TREES.

GO EAT THEM!

GASP!

BUT...WHAT IF THEY'RE *POISONOUS?*

DON'T TEASE ME.

NOW, GET OFF MY LAWN!

SLAM

I DIDN'T SEE THAT COMING.

I'M STILL HUNGRY!

ARE AVOCADOS...

I WANNA GO HOME!

I'M ALLERGIC TO GRASS!

STOP ASKING THAT!

SO, WHAT DO WE DO NOW?

ANYONE?

I MEAN, WE'VE GOTTA DO SOMETHING!

HEY, YOU! YOU LOOK KINDA SMART...

UH...THANKS?

WHADDA YOU THINK WE SHOULD DO?!

OH...I...I... DON'T KNOW.

IT'S ALL HAPPENING SO FAST...LET ME THINK...

WELL, FIRST WE SHOULD PROBABLY BUILD A FIRE AND MAKE A SHELTER...

HEY, DAD?

WHY DON'T WE ASK RED?

I MEAN... SHE SAVED US FROM THE SANDSTORM AND THE BLUE CREATURES.

AND SHE DID GET US TO THIS VALLEY.

THE ADVENTURE CONTINUES IN *RED'S PLANET BOOK TWO: FRIENDS AND FOES* COMING SPRING 2017